Collins

Easy Learning

Spelling

Age 5-7

My name is _____ .

I am _____ years old.

I go to _____ School.

Karina Law

How to use this book

- Find a quiet, comfortable place to work, away from other distractions.
- Tackle one topic at a time.
- Help with reading the instructions where necessary, and ensure that your child understands what to do.
- Encourage your child to check their own answers as they complete each activity.
- Discuss with your child what they have learnt.
- Let your child return to their favourite pages once they have been completed, to talk about the activities.
- Reward your child with plenty of praise and encouragement.

Special features

Yellow boxes: Introduce a topic and outline the key spelling ideas.

 Suggests when a dictionary may be needed for help with spelling.

Learning a new word

When your child is learning a new word, help them to practise using the 'Look and say, cover, write, check' method.

- Look at the word and say it aloud.
- Cover it.
- Write it.
- Check it.

You could also try the following ideas:

- Break the word up into smaller parts, for example, cup-board.
- Pronounce the word exactly as it is written, for example, Wed-nes-day.
- Break the word up into separate phonemes (sounds), for example, sh-ee-p.

Published by Collins
An imprint of HarperCollins*Publishers*
77–85 Fulham Palace Road
Hammersmith
London
W6 8JB

Browse the complete Collins catalogue at
www.collins.co.uk

10 9 8 7 6 5

ISBN-13 978-0-00-722262-9
ISBN-10 0-00-722262-9

The author asserts the moral right to be identified as the author of this work.

British Library Cataloguing in Publication Data
A Catalogue record for this publication is available from the British Library

Written by Karina Law
Design and layout by Graham M Brasnett
Illustrated by Andy Tudor
Printed and bound in China

Contents

Short vowels

There are five vowels.

a e i o u

Most words in the English language contain at least one vowel.

Q1 Write the missing vowel in each word.

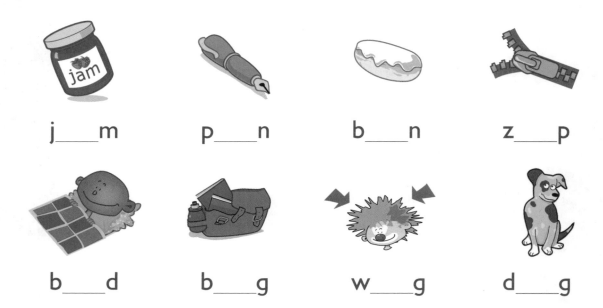

j___m   p___n   b___n   z___p

b___d   b___g   w___g   d___g

Q2 Change the vowel in each word to make a new word.

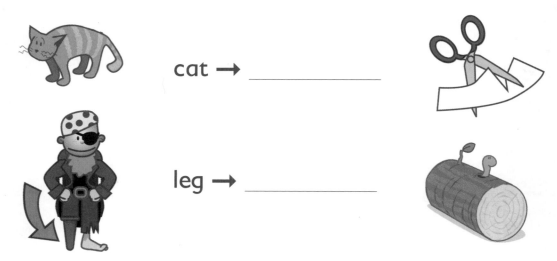

cat → _____

leg → _____

Rhyming words

Rhyming words end with the same sound.

a wet pet

Q1 Circle the picture that rhymes with the word.

bed

box

cap

Q2 Look at the circled words. Find the words that rhyme with them and circle them in the same colour.

hat   (sun)   peg   (bat)   win   beg   bin

pot   dot

(hot)   run   (leg)   rat   (tin)   fun

Long vowels with e

Say the word. Add the letter **e**. Say the new word.
Can you hear a change in the vowel sound?

  cap + e → cape

The vowel in c**a**p is a **short vowel**.
When we add **e** to this word, the first vowel becomes a **long vowel**.

Q1 Add **e** to the end of each word to make a new word.

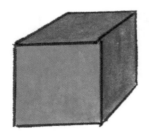

cub → cub____

not → not____

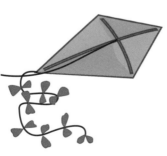

kit → kit____

plan → plan____

Q2 Write words that rhyme.

m
r
sh
+ ake

cake _____

_____ _____

c
st
thr
+ one

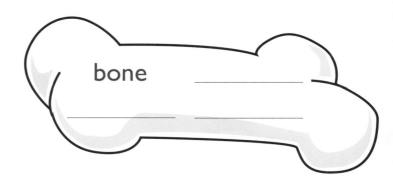

bone _____

_____ _____

Q3 Change one letter to make a new word.

race ➜ ____ace

bake ➜ b____ke

nose ➜ ____ose

fire ➜ fi____e

5

mule ➜ m____le

mice ➜ ____ice

Spelling patterns: sh, ch, th

Listen to **sh**, **ch** and **th** in these words.

sheep   cheese   thumb

Q1 Join **sh** and **ch** to the things that start with their sound.

ch   **sh**

What does a
sea monster eat
for lunch?

Fish and ships!

Q2 Write **sh**, **ch** or **th** at the end of each word.

fi_____   bea_____   pa_____   bru_____

ru_____   mo_____   fini_____   lun_____

Word ending: ck

Listen to the sound of **ck** at the end of clo**ck**.

The spelling pattern **ck** is only used after a short vowel.

Q1 Complete the rhymes. Choose a **ck** word to write in each space.

sock   clock   stuck   struck

Hickory Dickory Dock,
A mouse ran up the _____.
The clock _____ one,
The mouse ran down,
Hickory Dickory Dock.

Hickory Dickory Dock,
A mouse chewed a hole in my _____.
My toe _____ out,
The mouse ran about,
Hickory Dickory Dock.

Q2 Read the **ck** words in the wall below.

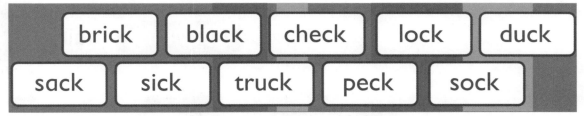

brick	black	check	lock	duck
sack	sick	truck	peck	sock

Colour the bricks. Use a different colour for each pair of rhyming words.

Word ending: ng

Listen to the sound of **ng** at the end of ri**ng**.

Q1 Lots of noisy words end in **ng**. Write **ng** at the end of each word.

ba___!

cla___!

do___!

di___!

bo___!

Q2 Cross out the wrong word.

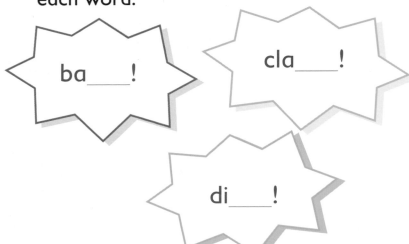

A (strong string) man.

Very (lung long) hair.

A very loud (pong song) .

Word endings: ff, ll, ss

These words all end with a **double consonant**.

gruff

well

princess

The double consonant in each word makes a single sound.

Q1 Write **ff**, **ll** or **ss** in each space.

Humpty Dumpty sat on a wa____,

Humpty Dumpty had a big fa____.

The prince____ gave the

frog a ki____.

I'll hu____ and I'll pu____ and I'll blow your

house down!

Why is Cinderella
no good at hockey?

**Because she is
always running away
from the ball!**

More than one

We usually add **s** to the end of a word when there is more than one of something.

one leg   lots of legs

For a word that ends in **s**, **x**, **sh** or **ch**, we usually add **es**.

bus**es**   fox**es**   brush**es**   peach**es**

Q1 Add **s** or **es** to the end of each word.

a pair of sock____

a bunch of
banana____

some sweet____

dish____

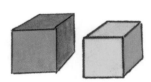

box____

monster____

sandwich____

spider____

octopus____

Colour words

Q1 Label the balloons.

red   yellow   pink   green   blue   orange   purple

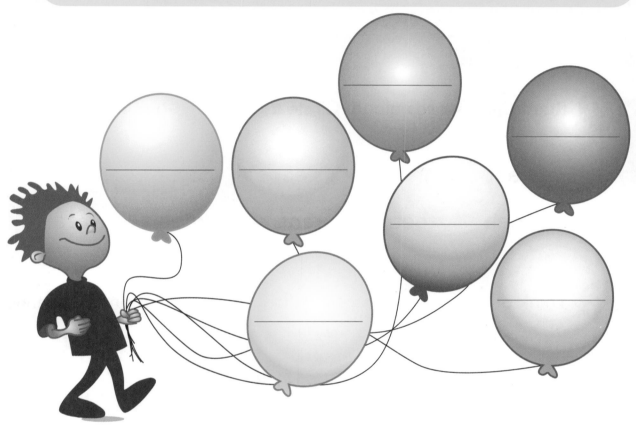

Q2 Unscramble the letters and write the colours.

wnrbo   ewith   cklab

_____   _____   _____

Vowel sound: ee, ea

Listen to the sound of **ee** in b**ee**.

Listen to the same sound of **ea** in b**ea**d.

Q1 Read these words aloud. Circle the odd one out in each row.

sweet	green	sleep	fence	street
queen	teeth	tent	knee	free

Q2 Think of three more words with **ee**. Write them on the beehive.

bee

Q3 Read these words aloud. Colour the odd one out in each row.

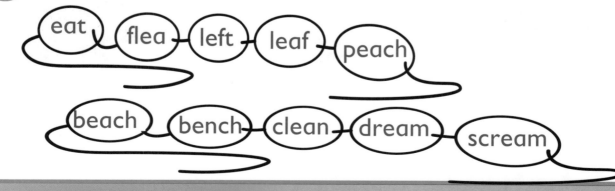

eat   flea   left   leaf   peach

beach   bench   clean   dream   scream

Vowel sound: ai, ay

Listen to the sound of **ai** in sn**ai**l.

The **ai** sound is usually spelt **ay** at the end of words.

Listen to the same sound of **ay** in pl**ay**.

Q1 Use the letters below to write words that rhyme with **snail**.

m
t
n
tr
fr

+ ail

snail

_____

_____

_____

_____

_____

Q2 Write **ai** or **ay** in these words.

tr____   tr____n   tod____

aw____   afr____d   s____

cl____   st____   p____nt

Vowel sound: ie, y, igh

Listen to the sound of **ie** in p**ie**.

Listen to the sound of **y** in fl**y**.

Listen to the same sound of **igh** in h**igh**.

Q1 Write rhyming words with **y** or **ie**.

fly   cr_____   t_____   fly

fr_____   p_____   sp_____

tr_____   wh_____   l_____

What is the difference between a bird and a fly?

A bird can fly but a fly can't bird!

Q2 Write rhyming words with **igh**.

n_____ _____ _____ _____   fr_____ _____ _____ _____

fl_____ _____ _____ _____   br_____ _____ _____ _____

l_____ _____ _____ _____   m_____ _____ _____ _____

r_____ _____ _____ _____   s_____ _____ _____ _____

knight

Q3 Finish the sentences. Write a word with **igh** in each space.

My shoes are too t_____ _____ _____ _____ .

The train ride gave me a fr_____ _____ _____ _____ .

Vowel sound: oa, ow

Listen to the sound of **oa** in b**oa**t.

Listen to the same sound of **ow** in yell**ow**.

Q1 Use these words to complete the word puzzle below.

> sparrow   coat   arrow   moat   elbow   toast   snow   coast

1 You use this to bend your arm.

2 A ditch filled with water that surrounds a castle.

3 A slice of bread heated until it turns brown.

4 A small brown bird.

5 Where the land meets the sea.

6 A pointed stick with feathers on the end.

7 White, frozen water that falls from the sky.

8 You wear this over your other clothes.

Q2 Now find three pairs of rhyming words in the word puzzle and write them in the spaces below.

1 _____   _____

2 _____   _____

3 _____   _____

Vowel sound: oo, ew, ue

Listen to the sound of **oo** in b**oo**t.

Listen to the sound of **ew** in n**ew**.

Listen to the same sound of **ue** in bl**ue**.

Q1 Circle words with **oo**, **ew** and **ue**.

i	f	e	w	x	p	i	z	o	o
y	s	s	o	o	n	c	d	w	q
j	p	h	r	e	s	c	u	e	a
m	m	w	p	b	z	g	l	u	e
o	c	h	e	w	t	t	p	l	k
m	o	o	n	g	a	r	g	u	e
q	l	x	g	l	f	l	e	w	r
j	e	w	e	l	j	s	e	m	f
t	i	s	s	u	e	p	o	h	l
a	a	y	c	o	o	l	f	m	s

Q2 Write the words you have circled in the table below.

oo	ew	ue

18

Spelling pattern: ar

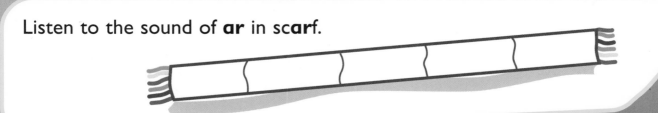

Listen to the sound of **ar** in sc**ar**f.

Q1 Write the letters below in the **ar** words on the scarf.

p   ch   m   g   y

far____   shar____   part____   mar____   ____arden

Q2 Use the letters below to write rhyming words inside the shark and the star.

c   p   j   d   m   f

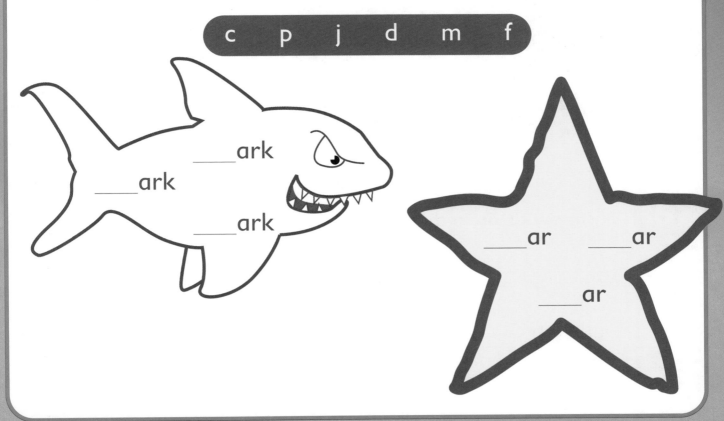

____ark

____ark

____ark

____ar   ____ar

____ar

OW, OU

Listen to the sound of **ow** in **ow**l.

Listen to the same sound of **ou** in m**ou**se.

Q1 Read the rhyme aloud. Underline ten **ow** and **ou** words.

"Watch out!" called a cat
To a mouse by a tree,
"There's an owl on the prowl.
Why not hang out with me?"

So the mouse jumped down
From his hiding place.
The cat pounced and Mouse
Disappeared without a trace.

What did the owl say to his friend as he flew away?

"Owl be seeing you later!"

Q2 Write **ow** or **ou** in these words.

d___n   f___nd   br___n   h___se

cl___n   sh___er   c___nt   fl___er

v___el   m___th   s___nd   t___n

20

air, are, ear, ere

These rhyming words all share the same sound but have a different spelling pattern.

chair **sp**are **b**ear **th**ere

Q1 Write these words in the correct column.

wear there repair tear stair scare where spare

air	are	ear	ere

Some words sound the same but are spelt differently.

Where is my hat?

I want to **wear** it to the match.

Why did the doll blush?

Because she saw the teddy bear!

Q2 Circle the correct word to label each picture.

pear pair

hair hare

stair stare

bear bare

21

or, oor, aw, au, ore

These words all share the same sound but have a different spelling pattern.

for   door   paw   naughty   more

Q1 Write **or** in these words.

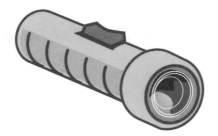

t____ch   f____k

st____y   st____m   st____k

Q2 Say these words out loud. Circle the odd one out.

lawn   dawn   thorn

down   corn   yawn

Q3 Join up the rhyming words.

floor   crawl   sport   caught   draw

short   snore   taught   law   shawl

er, ir, ur

These words all share the same sound but have a different spelling pattern.

tiger

bird

turtle

Q1 Label the pictures. Then write the words in the table. Add one more of your own in each column.

sh_____

P_____

m_____

d_____

th_____

t_____

er	ir	ur

23

wh, ph, ch

Listen to the sound of **wh** in **wh**ale.

Listen to the sound of **ph** in ele**ph**ant.

Listen to the sound of **ch** in or**ch**estra.

Q1 These labels are spelt wrongly. Write the correct word.

dolfin *x* _____

weel *x* _____

quoir *x* _____

scool *x* _____

Lots of question words begin with **wh**.

who   what   when   where   why   which

Q2 Join each question to the correct answer.

1 **Wh**ere do children go to learn?   A **ch**emist

2 **Wh**ich animal is the largest   A **sch**ool
   sea creature?

3 **Wh**y might you use a camera?   A **wh**ale

4 **Wh**at do we call the letters a   To take a **ph**oto
   to z?

5 **Wh**o might you buy   The al**ph**abet
   medicine from?

Q3 Write the meaning of each of these words.
The first one has been done for you.

sphere   An object that is round like a ball.

graph   _____

echo   _____

ache   _____

wheat   _____

whistle   _____

ear (hear), ea (head)

Listen to the sound of **ear** in h**ear**.

Q1 Use the letters below to make words that rhyme with **ear**.

y
d
n
f
sp
g
cl
r
app
t

_____   _____

_____   _____

_____   _____

_____   _____

_____   _____

Listen to the sound of **ea** in h**ea**vy.

Q2 Join each word to a matching picture.

head

weather

bread

breakfast

Compound words

A compound word is a word made up of two other words.

 newspaper

Q1 Join up the words to make new words.

water	cup	waterfall
tooth	house	_____
light	fall	_____
egg	day	_____
birth	brush	_____

Q2 Write the missing compound word in each joke.

> jellyfish   honeycomb   football   sunglasses

Why did the teacher wear _____?
Because her class was so bright!

Why did the _____ player wear a bib?
Because he was always dribbling!

What do _____ say at the start of a race?
Get set!

Why did the bee have sticky hair?
Because of his _____!

Prefixes: un, dis

We can add **un** and **dis** in front of some words to change their meaning and make **opposite** words.

tidy

untidy

appear

disappear

Q1 Finish writing the label under each picture.

un_____

un_____

un_____

un_____

Q2 Write **un** or **dis** in front of each word to make an opposite word.

____pack   ____agree   ____lucky   ____kind

____honest   ____fair   ____true   ____sure

Suffixes: ful, ly

We can add **ful** and **ly** to the end of some words to make describing words.

careful

quietly

'shhh'

There is no word in English ending in -**full** except full!

Q1 Add **ful** or **ly** to each word.

pain____   silent____   sudden____

help____   quick____   thought____

exact____   slow____   forget____

Q2 Now choose a word to label each picture.

_____

_____

_____

_____

Spelling tips

Silly sentences can help you remember how to spell a word.

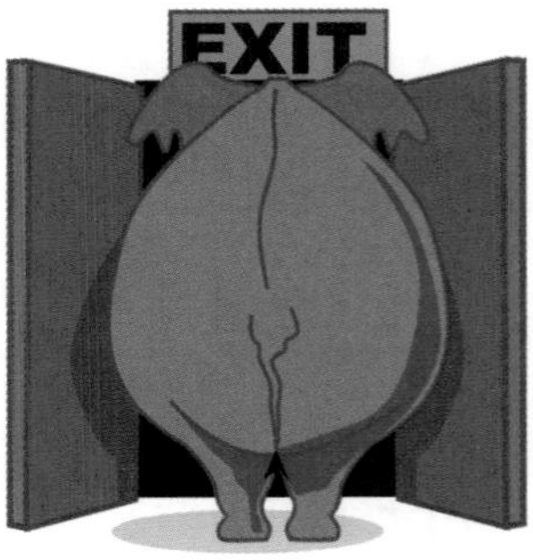

big elephants can't always use small exits → because!

gentle elephants never tackle little elephants → gentle!

Q1 Finish these silly sentences to help you remember how to spell **people** and **beauty**.

pink	big
elephants	elephants
o______________	a______________
p______________	u______________
l______________	t______________
e______________	y______________

Look for words inside words.

I like **ice** in my ju**ice**.

Q2 Underline a smaller word inside each of these words.

monkey   when   garage   chocolate

danger   brilliant   cupboard   comfortable

Q3 Hide each of these words inside a larger word.

put   <u>**computer**</u>   elf _____   pin _____

owl _____   ear _____   itch _____

Watch out for silent letters.

com**b**

Q4 Circle the silent letter inside each of these words.

thumb   knee   write   honest

knit   castle   autumn   knight

Answers

Short vowels

Page 4

Q1 jam, pen, bun, zip
bed, bag, wig, dog

Q2 cat – cut, leg – log

Rhyming words

Page 5

Q1 red, fox, map

Q2 hat, sun, peg, bat, win, beg, bin
pot, dot
hot, run, leg, rat, tin, fun

Long vowels with e

Page 6

Q1 cube, note, kite, plane

Page 7

Q2

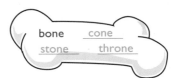

cake   make
rake   shake

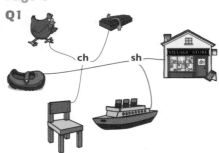

bone   cone
stone   throne

Q3 face, bike, rose, five, mole, dice

Spelling patterns: sh, ch, th

Page 8

Q1

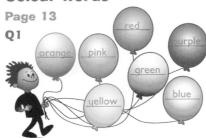

ch   sh

Q2 fish, beach, path, brush
rush, moth, finish, lunch

Word ending: ck

Page 9

Q1 A mouse ran up the clock
The clock struck one
A mouse chewed a hole in my sock
My toe stuck out

Q2 brick – sick, black – sack,
check – peck, lock – sock,
duck – truck

Word ending: ng

Page 10

Q1 bang, clang, dong, ding, bong

Q2 strong, long, song

Word ending: ff, ll, ss

Page 11

Q1 wall, fall
princess, kiss
huff, puff

More than one

Page 12

Q1 socks, bananas, sweets,
dishes, boxes, monsters,
sandwiches, spiders, octopuses

Colour words

Page 13

Q1

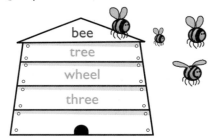

red, purple, orange, pink, green, yellow, blue

Q2 brown, white, black

Vowel sound: ee, ea

Page 14

Q1 fence, tent

Q2 possible answers are:

bee
tree
wheel
three

Q3 left, bench

Vowel sound: ai, ay

Page 15

Q1

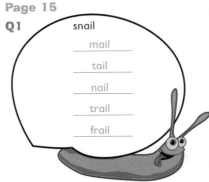

snail
mail
tail
nail
trail
frail

Q2 tray, train, today
away, afraid, say
clay, stay, paint

Vowel sound: ie, y, igh

Page 16

Q1 fly, cry, tie
fry, pie, spy
try, why, lie

Q2 night, fright
flight, bright
light, might
right, sight

Q3 tight, fright

Vowel sound: oa, ow

Page 17

Q1

					1e			2m
					l			o
					b			a
		3t	o	a	s	t		
					w		4p	
							a	
			5c				r	
6a	r	r	o	w			r	
			a				7s	n	o	w
8c	o	a	t					

Q2 1 moat, coat
2 arrow, sparrow
3 toast, coast